1 3 5 7 9 10 8 6 4 2

First published in the United Kingdom in 1997 by
Julia MacRae
Random House, 20 Vauxhall Bridge Road, London SW1V 2SA

Random House Australia (Pty) Limited
20 Alfred Street, Milsons Point, Sydney,
New South Wales 2061, Australia

Random House New Zealand Limited
18 Poland Road, Glenfield,
Auckland 10, New Zealand

Random House South Africa (Pty) Limited
Endulini, 5A Jubilee Road, Parktown 2193, South Africa

Random House UK Limited Reg. No. 954009

A CIP catalogue record for this book
is available from the British Library

ISBN 1-85681-553-6

Printed in Singapore
by Tien Wah Press (Pte) Ltd

Why do stars come out at night?

ANNALENA McAFEE

with illustrations by

ANTHONY LEWIS

JM

Julia MacRae Books

LONDON SYDNEY AUCKLAND JOHANNESBURG

Why is the sky so high?

Because the clouds would get caught in your hair.

Why do fish swim?

Because they've forgotten how to dance.

Why is the sea wet?

Because the mermaids wash their pearls.

Why is the grass green?

Because they ran out of blue.

Why is the sun hot?

Because it's been chasing around the earth.

Why do stars come out at night?

Because the moon is scared of the dark.

Why do we fall asleep?

Because our dreams must go out to play.

Why do babies cry?

Because they don't know how to sing.

Why do grown-ups get cross?

Because they haven't been kissed all week.

Why do children go to school?

Because teachers get lonely without them.

Why is the snow so cold?

Because the clouds forgot to wrap up.

Why are trees so tall?

Because they're trying to catch the birds.

Why do the birds fly?

Because they have to hold up the sky.

Why is the sky so high?